Pengu

# UNLOCKING THE UNIVERSE

## STEPHEN & LUCY HAWKING

LEVEL

5

ADAPTED BY CATRIN MORRIS
ILLUSTRATED BY JAN BIELECKI
SERIES EDITOR: SORREL PITTS

PENGUIN BOOKS

UK | USA | Canada | Ireland | Australia
India | New Zealand | South Africa

Penguin Books is part of the Penguin Random House group of companies
whose addresses can be found at global.penguinrandomhouse.com.
www.penguin.co.uk www.puffin.co.uk www.ladybird.co.uk

*Unlocking the Universe* first published by Puffin Books, 2020
This Penguin Readers edition published by Penguin Books Ltd, 2021
001

Original text written by Stephen Hawking and Lucy Hawking
Text for Penguin Readers edition adapted by Catrin Morris
Copyright © Lucy Hawking, 2020
Text copyright Penguin Books Ltd, 2021
Illustrations and diagrams by Jan Bielecki
Cover image copyright © Penguin Books Ltd, 2019

This Penguin Readers edition of *Unlocking the Universe*
has adapted material from the following sources:
'What You Need to Know about Black Holes' by Professor Stephen Hawking, first published in
*George's Secret Key to the Universe* (Corgi Books, 2007);
'Why Do We Go into Space?' by Professor Stephen Hawking, 'A Voyage Across the Universe'
by Professor Bernard Carr, 'Getting in Touch with Aliens' by Dr Seth Shostak, and 'Is There Anyone Out There?'
by Lord Martin Rees, first published in *George's Cosmic Treasure Hunt* (Corgi Books, 2009);
'The Creation of the Universe' by Professor Stephen Hawking and 'Wormholes and Time Travel'
by Dr Kip S. Thorne, first published in *George and the Big Bang* (Corgi Books, 2011);
'The Building Blocks of Life' by Dr Toby Blench, first published in
*George and the Unbreakable Code* (Corgi Books, 2014);
'Volcanoes on Earth, in our Solar System and Beyond' by Professor Tamsin A. Mather,
'Imagining a Life on Mars' by Kellie Gerardi, 'The Overview Effect' by Dr Richard Garriott de Cayeux, first
published in *George and the Blue Moon* (Corgi Books, 2016);
'Climate Change' by Nitya Kapadia, first published in the original edition of
*Unlocking the Universe* (Puffin Books, 2020)

The moral right of the original authors and the original illustrator has been asserted

Printed and bound in Great Britain by Clays Ltd, Elcograf S.p.A.

The authorized representative in the EEA is Penguin Random House Ireland,
Morrison Chambers, 32 Nassau Street, Dublin D02 YH68

A CIP catalogue record for this book is available from the British Library

ISBN: 978–0–241–49319–9

All correspondence to:
Penguin Books
Penguin Random House Children's
One Embassy Gardens, 8 Viaduct Gardens,
London SW11 7BW

# Contents

# Note about the book

Stephen Hawking was one of the world's greatest thinkers. He studied and taught maths and physics at the University of Cambridge. He died in March 2018. His daughter, Lucy, uses stories to help explain science to more people.

Their book takes us on a journey of the **Universe**\*, through **space** and time. It starts 13.8 billion years ago with the Big Bang, which led to the **stars**, the **planets** and our **Solar System** being **formed**. It introduces us to the people who helped us to learn more about the Universe. Then, it explores our Solar System and other solar systems – the ones we know and others we have yet to find.

It introduces us to some **complex** ideas about our Universe: why it is **expanding** more quickly than we once thought, and what black holes and **wormholes** are. It explains why there is life on the Earth and thinks about other places where we, or aliens, could maybe live and how to get there.

Finally, it leaves us with some big questions about the Universe – some that we may never be able to answer.

\*Definitions of words in **bold** can be found in the glossary on pages 89—93.

# Before-reading questions

1 How much do you know about our Solar System?
   Can you name the eight planets and put them in the correct
   order from the Sun?

2 Where would you like to visit in space? Give your reasons.

3 What do we need for life on the Earth, do you think?

4 If you could travel through space and time, would you
   prefer to go into the past or the future? Why?

5 The title of this book is *Unlocking the Universe*. What secrets
   do you think that it might unlock?

6 What secrets would you like to discover about the Universe?

CHAPTER ONE
# Introducing the Universe

The word "**universe**" comes from an old word that means "everything". The Universe for us today is everything around us on the Earth and up in **space**. Everything that we can see if we look up at the sky, like the Sun, the Moon, the **stars** and the other **planets** of our **Solar System**, is in the Universe. And everything that we can see with a very **powerful telescope**, like the Milky Way **Galaxy**, is in it, too.

Our Solar System is in the Milky Way Galaxy, but there are other galaxies **further** away that maybe we cannot actually see at all, and these are also part of the Universe.

How we think about the Universe has changed a lot over the years. In the past, people had very different ideas about it. More than 2,000 years ago, the Greek Aristotle believed that the Earth was the centre of the Universe. Not everybody agreed with him, but for more than a thousand years, most people thought that Aristotle's idea was correct.

Then, in the 16th century, the Polish **astronomer** Copernicus showed that the Earth and other planets **orbited** the Sun. This was a new idea that made the Sun suddenly seem more important than the Earth.

In the 16th century, astronomers thought that our Galaxy, the Milky Way, was just a cloudy line of light in the sky and nothing more. But, when the Italian astronomer Galileo looked through his own telescope a few years after Copernicus, he saw that in the Milky Way there were millions of stars. Galileo discovered that the Sun had a less important position in the whole Universe, because the Universe was much bigger than people had thought it was before.

By the 18th century, people believed that the Milky Way was a circle of stars that were held together by **gravity**. But most astronomers still thought of the Milky Way as the whole Universe, with nothing outside it.

Then, in 1924, Edwin Hubble, an American astronomer, **measured** the **distance** between our Galaxy and the next big galaxy, called Andromeda. He discovered that Andromeda was too far away to be a part of the Milky Way. So, once more, the Universe had grown!

Hubble also found information about several other galaxies near the Milky Way. He discovered that the Universe is **expanding**, and that the further away from us a galaxy is, the faster it is moving away. So, the speed at which galaxies move away from our Galaxy can tell us how far away from us they are. This is called Hubble's Law. Astronomers have used Hubble's Law to find the distance of a part of the Universe that is tens of billions of **light years** away, where there are hundreds of billions of other galaxies that we have not yet discovered.

But how and when did our Universe begin? Most astronomers agree that it began about 13.8 billion years ago with the Big Bang. At that time, the **matter**, which

**The Andromeda Galaxy is the nearest
large galaxy to the Milky Way.**

things in the Universe are made of, was very hot and pressed together. The moment when this matter started to expand is called the Big Bang. During a very early stage, called "inflation", the expansion happened so quickly that the Universe became very **smooth** and flat. But it was not totally smooth, so the **temperature** was a little different in different places. This also meant that some parts of the Universe grew more slowly than other parts. When the slower parts stopped expanding, they **collapsed** to **form** galaxies, stars and planets, and because of that we have life on Earth.

Our Solar System was formed when a cloud of **dust** started to collapse. This was maybe **caused** by a supernova – a star that **explodes** and becomes very bright. Then, a ball of this dust turned round and round, until it became a very flat circle. As the circle **attracted** more dust, it got bigger and turned more quickly.

The middle of the circle got hotter and hotter, until it started to burn and became a star. As the star burned, the dust in the circle around it slowly held together to form rocks. These rocks finally became planets, which all orbited the bright star in the middle – our Sun.

These planets formed groups. In the first group, near the Sun where it is hotter, the planets are made of rocks. In the second group, far away from the Sun, are the gas planets, which have gas on the outside and **liquid** inside them. Furthest from the Sun are the ice planets, which have ice and gas.

The planets cleaned their path round the Sun by attracting all the bits of rock that got in their way. Hundreds of millions of years later, the planets had developed **clear** paths, or **orbits**, round the Sun.

## CHAPTER TWO

# People who helped us to discover the Universe

### Galileo Galilei

Galileo Galilei (1564–1642) was born near Pisa in Italy, although his family came from Florence. He was studying to be a doctor before he changed to maths and philosophy – the study of the meaning of life. When he was just eighteen, he watched a light high on the ceiling in Pisa Cathedral. It was moving from side to side, and each time it moved it took the same number of seconds before it changed direction, however far it actually travelled. He used this information to help develop better clocks. There is also a famous story about Galileo and the Tower of Pisa. According to the story, Galileo climbed to the top of the tower and dropped stones from it. He discovered that the speed they fell in a straight line was the same for any size or **weight** of stone.

Galileo developed a new telescope, which marked the true start of **astronomy**. With his telescope, Galileo discovered many things in space.

In 1610, he saw four moons orbiting the planet Jupiter. So, he realized that not everything in the Solar System went around the Earth as people had believed before. This totally changed the idea of the Earth's place in the Solar System and in the Universe itself. Another astronomer,

Simon Marius, who discovered the moons just one day after Galileo, named them Io, Europa, Ganymede and Callisto.

Galileo also discovered that Saturn did not look like other planets, because it had rings around it. He could not see these rings very well because Saturn is even further away from Earth than Jupiter. So, for a while, he thought that the planet had ears and not rings!

In 1989, the Galileo space **probe** was **launched**, which was named after the famous astronomer. In 1995, it finally arrived at Jupiter and spent 8 years studying the planet and its moons. It sent back lots of information about Jupiter's fourth-largest moon, Europa. Galileo was also the first space probe to fly near an **asteroid**, and the first to discover an asteroid with a moon.

### Isaac Newton

Sir Isaac Newton (1642–1727) was born in England. His father died when he was a child, so he was looked after by his grandmother. At school, he enjoyed discovering new things. He studied maths and physics, and he also developed a new kind of telescope. There is a famous story about Newton, too. When he saw an apple fall off a tree at home, it helped him to understand the laws of gravity – a **theory** he had developed by the time he was just twenty-three years old.

In 1687, Newton wrote two important ideas: the Laws of Motion, which describe the way that things move; and the Law of Gravitation, which explains how everything in the

Universe attracts other things through the **force** of gravity. Gravity keeps us on the **surface** of the Earth, it keeps the Earth orbiting the Sun, and it leads to new stars and planets being born. Newton was also the first person to write about the maths behind an **artificial satellite** – an idea he called "Newton's Cannonball". Newton's laws still help scientists send satellites into space and **spaceships** to other planets today. And we still measure the force of things in newtons (N).

### Albert Einstein

Albert Einstein (1879–1955) was given the Nobel Prize in Physics in 1921. He was born in Germany, but his family moved first to Italy and then to Switzerland. He was interested in science when he was really young. At only five years old, he already wanted to know about lots of different types of technology. At twelve, he was teaching himself **complex** maths, and he continued to study physics and maths after that. Einstein left Europe and went to the United States of America in 1933, just before Adolf Hitler started leading Germany. He stayed in the USA for the rest of his life, and he became an American. Einstein believed in peace and not war, and worked for peace all his life.

When he was twenty-six, Einstein wrote three important papers about science. He also developed two important theories about space and time. The first, in 1905, was his "special theory of relativity". This theory was that nothing could travel faster than the speed of light. This means it would take at least 100,000 years to cross the Galaxy and 10 billion years to cross the Universe. But special relativity also means that time moves more slowly for people who are moving, which means that this journey would take less time for the **astronauts** than for the people back home on Earth.

Just imagine, if the astronauts could actually travel at the speed of light, no time would pass for the travellers at all. But that is impossible according to Einstein's theory. So, if the astronauts travelled at a little less than the speed of light, time for them would just be much shorter than for the people on Earth. For example, a journey across the Milky Way Galaxy might take 30 years for the astronauts, but, when they returned to Earth, all their friends and families would be long dead.

Einstein's other important theory, written in 1915, was his "general theory of relativity", and it is even more exciting. This theory could mean that astronauts might one day be able to time-travel by using something called **wormholes**, which we will read more about later. So, you could maybe

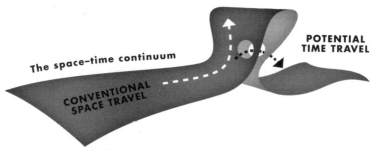

How time travel could work

travel across space faster, and get back to Earth before your friends and family died. But that is just a theory, and it has not been shown to be true yet!

### Edwin Hubble

Edwin Hubble (1889–1953) was an American astronomer. At school, Hubble was not only good at science, he was also good at sport and other school subjects, although he was not good at spelling. He worked at the Mount Wilson Observatory in California, USA. An observatory is a place where astronomers study space through telescopes.

In 1923, Hubble used an enormous telescope called the Hooker Telescope to look at the Andromeda Nebula. A nebula is a huge bright cloud of dust and gas. While he was looking through the Hooker, Hubble found a special kind of star called a Cepheid variable star in the Andromeda Nebula. This allowed him to measure the distance between the Earth and the Andromeda Nebula as 900,000 light years. Since then, the distance has been measured again as more than 2 million light years away, but it was still an important new piece of information about space. Hubble knew that the Andromeda Nebula could not possibly be in our Galaxy, because the furthest point of the Milky Way is only 52,850 light years from its centre. So, he realized that he was actually looking at a galaxy – which we now call the Andromeda Galaxy. This was the first of many galaxies that Hubble and other astronomers went on to find, each with billions and billions of stars in them.

Hubble also discovered a way of putting galaxies in groups according to their shape. And he found that the further away a galaxy was from the Solar System, the faster it travelled. This is called Hubble's Law. The first large space observatory to orbit the Earth, the Hubble Space Telescope, was named after Edwin Hubble.

## CHAPTER THREE
# The sky above us

During the daytime, only one bright star can be seen in the sky. It is the star that is nearest to us, and the star that is the most important in our daily lives. We have a special name for it – the Sun.

The Moon and the planets do not **shine** on their own. They appear bright at night because the Sun lights them up. All the other shining points in the night sky are stars, like our Sun. Some are bigger, some are smaller, but they are all stars. If there is no cloud in the sky at night, and you are away from city lights, you can see thousands of stars without using a telescope. You can also see a few other things that are not stars: the Moon and some of the planets, like Venus, Mars, Jupiter or Saturn.

Our Moon is a natural satellite of our planet. A satellite orbits something, like the Earth goes round the Sun; and "natural" means that it was not made by people. The Moon orbits the Earth in 27.3 days. But we only ever see the same side of the Moon when we look at it from Earth. From the Moon, the sky always looks black because there is no **atmosphere**.

The Moon is much smaller than the Earth. You could put forty-nine Moons into the Earth. It also has less gravity than the Earth. If your weight were 45 kilograms on the Earth, it would be 7.5 kilograms on the Moon.

The Moon was probably made more than 4 billion years ago when something the size of a planet hit the Earth. Scientists think this sent a hot cloud of dust and small pieces of rock into the Earth's orbit. As this cloud got cooler, parts of it held together until it finally formed the Moon.

You could not live on the Moon without wearing special clothes – a spacesuit – to protect you. And you would need water, although astronomers think that there is some ice on the Moon. Astronauts have landed on the Moon six times from the Earth.

In 1969, American astronauts Neil Armstrong and Buzz Aldrin became the first people to walk on the Moon.

People used to believe that the Moon was a mirror, or a bowl of fire, and that it was magic. And the Moon does do some magic on the Earth. The Moon's force of gravity makes the **tides** in the Earth's oceans. The sea on the side of the Earth nearest to the Moon is pulled harder towards the Moon, lifting up the water. This is high tide.

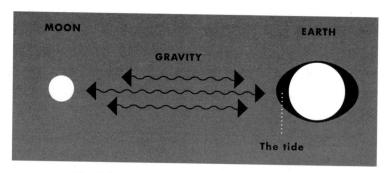

**The Moon's force of gravity on the Earth makes tides in the oceans.**

The Sun also helps with the tides. Although the Sun's force of gravity is much stronger than the Moon's, it is felt only about half as strongly, because the Sun is much further away from the Earth. But twice a month, when the Moon is in a line with the Earth and the Sun, the force of gravity of the Moon and the Sun work together to make large tides called spring tides.

———

Everything in our Universe takes time to travel. Light takes time, too. Light always travels in space at the speed of about 300,000 kilometres per second. This is called the speed of light. Light only takes about 1.3 seconds to travel from the Earth to the Moon, but it takes light from the Sun 8 minutes and 30 seconds to reach us on the Earth.

We measure distance in space in light years, which is the distance light travels in a year. A light year is about 9.5 trillion kilometres.

The other stars in the sky are much further away from the Earth than the Sun. The nearest star after the Sun is called Proxima Centauri. It takes 4.22 years for light from it to reach the Earth. All the other stars are even further away. The light of almost all the stars we can see in the night sky has been travelling for hundreds, thousands or tens of thousands of years before we see it. So, by the time we see them, some of the most distant stars might already be dead. But we do not know that yet, because the light the dying star has made has not reached us.

The Solar System is the area of space around our Sun.

In it are all the things attracted by the Sun's gravity and which orbit round it. There are planets, **dwarf planets**, moons, **comets**, asteroids, and other small things we have not discovered yet.

In 2006, the International Astronomical Union (IAU) decided to change the way that they described planets. A planet must orbit the Sun, and it has to be big enough for gravity to make it round and for it to stay that way. Its gravity must also attract almost everything that is near to it in space, so that there is no dust or rocks in its way as it orbits the Sun.

Pluto used to be thought of as a planet, but it is now called a dwarf planet because it has many rocks and other matter in its orbit. So now the eight planets of our Solar System, beginning with the nearest to the Sun, are: Mercury, Venus, Earth, Mars, Jupiter, Saturn, Uranus and Neptune.

As well as the planets and their moons, there are other things orbiting the Sun. Asteroids can be as small as pieces of dust or as big as dwarf planets. There is a big group of asteroids made of rock and metal, in what is called the asteroid belt. This is between Mars and Jupiter, and it may have almost 2 million asteroids in it that are larger than 1 kilometre in **diameter**. Some of the asteroids are big enough to have names, like the dwarf planet Ceres, which is 1,000 kilometres in diameter. Astronomers think that these asteroids are left from when the planets were first formed in the Solar System.

But there is a much bigger group of objects on the far

side of the planet Neptune. It is called the Kuiper Belt. It is twenty times as wide as the asteroid belt and maybe 200 times bigger than it. It is made of very small pieces of ice and gas, probably left from when the Solar System was formed. The dwarf planet Pluto can also be found in the Kuiper Belt.

———————

Planets that orbit stars different from our Sun are called exoplanets. By 2020, more than 4,000 exoplanets were discovered, and most of them are much bigger than the Earth. CoRoT-7b was discovered in 2009, and it was the first exoplanet that could be shown to be made of metal or rock.

Alpha Centauri is the closest star system to our Sun, at a little more than 4 light years away. Astronomers think it was formed 1,000 million years before our Solar System. It looks like there is just one star, but really there are three stars. Alpha Centauri A and Alpha Centauri B orbit the same point once every 80 years. There is also a third star, Proxima Centauri, which is the nearest to the Earth. It is called a red dwarf because it is a smaller, cooler star. It takes about a million years for Proxima Centauri to orbit the other two stars. There is an exoplanet orbiting Proxima Centauri. It is a little bigger than the Earth, and astronomers would really like to know if it has water or life on it. Astronomers think there might be a second exoplanet orbiting Proxima Centauri, too.

55 Cancri is a star system 41 light years away from us in

the direction of the Cancer constellation – a group of stars. 55 Cancri A is a yellow star, like the Sun; 55 Cancri B is a smaller, red dwarf star. These two stars orbit each other at 1,000 times the distance between the Earth and the Sun. This star system is a good example of a system with a family of planets in it.

In 1996, the first exoplanet orbiting Cancri A was discovered and named Cancri b. It is the size of Jupiter and orbits close to the star. In 2002, two more planets, Cancri c and Cancri d, were discovered. Then, in 2004, a fourth planet the size of Neptune was discovered and named Cancri e. This planet takes just 3 days to orbit the star Cancri A. It must be very hot, with surface temperatures up to 1,500°C.

On 6th November 2007, astronomers discovered a fifth planet orbiting Cancri A, and they called it Cancri f. This planet is a **giant** ball of gas, like Saturn in our Solar System. There may be moons in orbit around it, or planets like Earth made of rocks, where there could be water on the surface.

More exoplanets are being discovered all the time. Kepler-90, a star in the constellation Draco, has eight planets orbiting it. This is the same number of planets as in our Solar System. But could there be other constellations out there with more planets in them? Astronomers would love to know.

———

The Andromeda Galaxy, first discovered by Edwin

Hubble, is the nearest large galaxy to our own Milky Way. The Milky Way and Andromeda are in a group of at least forty galaxies that are near enough to feel the force of gravity from each other. The Milky Way and Andromeda are the two largest galaxies in the group.

Andromeda is different from most galaxies because the light coming from it looks blue. When something making light moves, it creates a **wave** of light that you can see. When the light is moving quickly towards you, the waves are shorter and look bluer. When the light is moving away from you, the waves are longer and look redder. So, astronomers think that Andromeda is moving towards the Milky Way at about 300 kilometres per second. In about 4.5 billion years, the two galaxies will meet each other and become one.

Some astronomers think that our Universe is part of a much bigger group of universes, which they sometimes call a multiverse. This theory was started in the 1920s, when astronomers discovered that our Universe is expanding. This means that more space developed in time. However, astronomers can only look at the stars and galaxies close enough to us in time and space. If there is a multiverse, other universes could be further away than this, and would not be something we can see now or will be able to see in the future. This is because it will take the light from those universes so much time to reach us that we will all be dead by the time that it arrives.

As you can imagine, the multiverse theory leads to all sorts of questions that are very difficult or impossible to answer. You could either think of it as one of the greatest science questions of our time, which one day astronomers will understand. Or you could think of it as not science at all, as some astronomers do, because you cannot jump from one universe to another.

## CHAPTER FOUR
# The Earth and why there is life on it

The Earth is formed of several **layers**. At the very centre is the part we call the inner core, which might be **solid**. Around it is the outer core, which is liquid. Further out is the mantle, made of very hot rock, which becomes liquid when the **pressure** is **released**. Above the mantle is the crust, which is covered by land and oceans. The crust is in several pieces, and these pieces are called tectonic plates. And all around the crust is the atmosphere.

The mantle is very hot, and, although it is solid, it can move slowly. But nature **melts** the hot rock in the Earth's mantle in two ways. In some places, like Iceland, tectonic plates move away from each other. Or deep underground in Hawaii, bits of hot mantle **flow** slowly up to the surface. In both Iceland and Hawaii, when there is less pressure on the rock, the rock begins to melt.

In other places, like underground in Japan and Indonesia, matter gets added to the mantle and makes it melt, just like when we add salt to roads in winter to melt the ice. This happens where two tectonic plates push together. One falls below the other and into the mantle, releasing water and other matter into the mantle rocks above it.

When the mantle melts, it forms a **liquid** rock called magma. This magma is not as **dense** as the rock around it, and so it starts to move up towards the surface.

This journey can be quite quick under the oceans, where the Earth's crust is thin. Or it can take longer where the crust is thicker, like on land. When the journey is longer, the magma has more time to become cool and less liquid.

But why does magma explode out of the ground instead of just coming out slowly like jam from the side of a cake? Magma has gases from water and carbon dioxide ($CO_2$) in it. As magma rises and the pressure falls, the gas begins to form **bubbles**. As they rise further, these bubbles grow bigger and bigger until they reach the surface and sometimes explode. The same thing happens when you shake a bottle of **fizzy** drink before you open it.

**The Earth's layers**

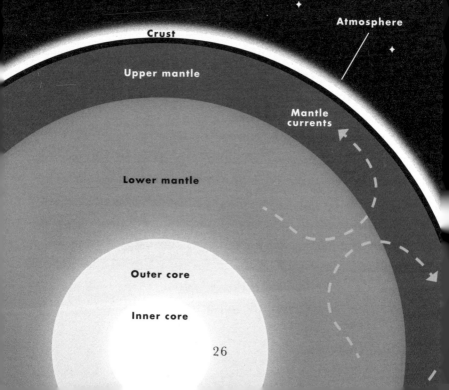

Atmosphere

Crust

Upper mantle

Mantle currents

Lower mantle

Outer core

Inner core

Some magmas are better at catching gas bubbles. This is why some **volcanoes erupt** much more quickly and are more dangerous than others.

When an active volcano erupts, first the ground shakes, and hot liquid called lava is pushed out of it. Then, you hear the sound of the gas trying to escape from the volcano. This is followed by the volcano exploding with a sound so loud that you can feel it through your body as well as your ears. The gas then hits you, making your eyes and nose hurt. And your skin starts to smell of the sulphur (S) coming out of the volcano, which is like bad eggs. Next, hot red rocks fly high into the sky, and they turn black as they get cooler and fall to the ground. Lava and rocks then flow down the side of the volcano.

But the Earth is not the only place in our Solar System that has volcanoes. Look at a full Moon in the night sky. The large, dark areas that you can see are solid lava beds called Maria, from an old word for "sea", because that is what they look like.

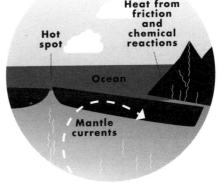

There are huge volcanoes on Mars, too, like Olympus Mons, the largest known volcano. It is about 600 kilometres wide and 22 kilometres high. That is two and a half times as high as Mount Everest, the highest mountain on the Earth, and about the size of the whole of Italy.

But, because the Moon and Mars are smaller than the Earth, they became cool more quickly, so their volcanoes have been dead for a long time.

Venus is nearly the same size as the Earth, so astronomers think that there may still be active volcanoes there. Further out in the Solar System, Jupiter has volcanoes on several of its more than sixty moons. One of the planet's larger moons, Io, has the most active volcano area in the whole of the Solar System. Its volcanoes send long clouds of gas and dust hundreds of kilometres into space. And astronomers also think that Europa, another of Jupiter's moons, probably has active ice volcanoes on it.

In 1989, the Voyager 2 space probe saw dark clouds rising high above one of Neptune's moons, Triton. And in 2005, the Cassini space probe saw gas and ice shooting into space from one of Saturn's moons, Enceladus.

Astronomers have now discovered exoplanets made of rocks outside our Solar System. This means that there might be other types of volcano out there in the Universe, which astronomers might learn about one day.

So far, the Earth is the only planet in the Universe where we know there is life. But what is needed for life? And why is there life on the Earth?

A **chemical element** is something pure that is made from just one type of **atom**. There are only 118 chemical elements that we know about, and everything in the world is made of one or more of these elements. The two smallest elements, hydrogen (H) and helium (He), were formed at the start of the Universe in the Big Bang. Some time after that, a large amount of these elements came together to form stars. In stars like the Sun, hydrogen burns at very high temperatures to make helium. So, as stars get older, they have more helium and less hydrogen in them. Then larger elements begin to form like carbon (C), nitrogen (N) and oxygen (O). Since human life is built on these elements, you could say that we are made of stars!

Very large, old stars finally collapse in on themselves, becoming so hot at the centre that they explode. We have met these stars before on page 10. They are called supernovas, and when they explode they release lots of **energy**. This energy is needed to make the heavier elements. Ninety-four of all the elements are formed in stars and are found naturally on the Earth. The other twenty-four elements are artificial.

Life (plants, animals and humans) is made from carbon, which is better than other elements at building complex **molecules** that can last in time. And there is a lot of carbon in the Universe. But you need more than just carbon for life. You need water, too. Around 60% of the human body is made of water, and it is important for making the body work correctly.

Amino acids are an important group of complex molecules, which we also need for life. Amino acids come together in different ways to form larger molecules, called **proteins**. These are found in all parts of the human body and do a lot of different jobs. Our hair is formed with proteins; they make our body strong and help it to move. They are also in the blood, and they help us to get the energy that we need from the food that we eat.

Temperature, too, is important for life, and it changes a lot in different places in space. The **average** temperature on the Earth's surface, where we live, is 15°C, while the average temperature on the surface of the Moon is 110°C in the day and -150°C at night. On the surface of the Sun, the average temperature is 5,500°C. And the average temperature in space is -270.4°C.

Gravity is also important for life and how you move about in different places.

Weight is the amount of gravity pulling you towards the Earth, while **mass** is the amount of matter that is inside you. On the Earth, we measure both weight and mass in kilograms. Really, we should measure our weight in newtons (N), because they describe the force of gravity, so a mass of 1 kilogram on Earth is about 10 newtons.

When you travel across the Solar System, your mass does not change but your weight does. So, when you **land** on a planet or moon with weaker gravity than the Earth, your weight changes although your mass stays the same. For example, if your weight was 34 kilograms on the Earth, it would be 5.6 kilograms on the Moon, 12.8 kilograms on Mars or Mercury, 30.6 kilograms on Venus and 80.3 kilograms on Jupiter. This means that you could jump very high on the Moon or on Mercury, but you would find it hard to take just one step on the ground on Jupiter. Or at least you would if Jupiter had solid ground, but it has not, because the planet is made of gas.

The Earth is the third closest planet to the Sun. Liquid water covers 70.8% of the surface of the Earth, and the rest is land. The average distance from the Earth to the Sun is 149.6 million kilometres, and it takes the Earth 365.25 days to orbit the Sun, which is called an Earth-year. All of these things and others mean that the Earth is in the Goldilocks Zone.

The name Goldilocks comes from the children's story about a hungry little girl who tried three bears' breakfasts and found one too cold, and another too hot, before finding one that was "just right". Then, she got tired, so she tried their beds. The first was too hard, the next one was too soft, and finally the third one was "just right".

In the same way, our planet Earth is "just right" for life. We get light from the Sun, which gives us heat. But we do not get so much heat that the atmosphere burns away, and the water turns into gas. And neither do we get so little heat that the water turns into ice, and it is impossible for us to live.

Water is liquid from 0°C, when it turns to ice, to 100°C, when it becomes a gas. Things cannot live without water.

It helps mix and release chemicals in many different **forms**, like proteins. Life is built on these.

There are four rock planets orbiting our Sun: Mercury, Venus, the Earth and Mars. But only the Earth has liquid water and life on it, because only the Earth is in the Goldilocks Zone.

Astronomers have found several thousand rock planets orbiting stars in our Milky Way Galaxy, and they think that there are many more – at least 100 billion. They are interested in finding planets in the Goldilocks Zone – the right distance from a planet's sun for the temperature not to be too hot and not too cold on the planet – to allow liquid water and possibly life.

Astronomers know that the exoplanet Cancri f is in the Goldilocks Zone. And they have seen many other planets like the Earth that may be in the Goldilocks Zone of their own stars. This would mean that they could have water on them and also life. But, at the moment, they are too far away for us to travel to them to explore them.

CHAPTER FIVE
# The other planets of our Solar System

## Mercury

Mercury is the smallest planet in our Solar System. Its diameter is 4,878 kilometres, so it is a little more than one third as wide as the Earth.

Mercury is also the closest planet to the Sun – on average 57.9 million kilometres away from it. Despite being so close to the Sun, Mercury is not the hottest planet in the Solar System; that is Venus. The temperature on Mercury goes from its hottest of 430°C, to its coldest of -170°C.

Mercury turns very slowly on its **axis**; each day lasts 59 Earth-days. But it orbits the Sun every 88 Earth-days, so its days are nearly as long as its years.

Mercury is made of rocks and is very dense, so it probably has an iron (Fe) core.

Its surface is a lot like the Moon's, with mountains, valleys, large, flat areas called plains, and large holes called craters on it. It has the biggest impact crater in the Solar System. An impact crater is a big hole formed by something hitting the planet hard. This crater, the Caloris Basin, is 1,550 kilometres in diameter. Opposite it is an area of strange hills, which astronomers call the "Weird Terrain". These were probably formed by the things that hit Mercury hard in the past. Between 2011 and 2015, the probe MESSENGER orbited Mercury, and it discovered water, in the form of ice, at its north pole.

The planets of our Solar System

## Venus

Venus is the second planet from the Sun, at an average distance of 108.2 million kilometres away. It is the hottest planet in the Solar System, with an average surface temperature of 462°C. The heat on the planet's surface cannot escape because its atmosphere experiences a **process** called the "greenhouse effect", with gases holding the heat in. The pressure in Venus's atmosphere is much higher than the Earth's, too, so there is no life or water on Venus.

As our closest neighbour, Venus is not much smaller than the Earth, with a diameter of around 12,000 kilometres. Venus turns very slowly on its axis – one day lasts 243 Earth-days. But it orbits the Sun in 225 Earth-days, so a day is longer than a year on Venus. It also orbits the Sun in the opposite direction to most other planets, and passes the Earth every 584 days.

Venus is the second-brightest thing in the night sky after the Moon, so it is easy for us to see. This is because the thick, **dense** atmosphere around the planet makes the light **shine** back to the Earth.

Space probes have discovered a lot of volcanoes on Venus, and two areas of high ground – one in the south and one in the north. Venus was the first planet to be visited by a probe (Mariner 2) in 1962 and the first to be landed on by a spacecraft (Venera 7) in 1970.

## Mars

After the Earth, Mars is the fourth planet from the Sun, at an average distance of 227.9 million kilometres away. It orbits the Sun once every 1.88 Earth-years, and it has two small moons called Phobos and Deimos.

The diameter of Mars is 6,805 kilometres, and it has an iron core. Between its core and its red crust is a thick layer of rocks. There is also a very thin atmosphere, mostly made of carbon dioxide, a gas that we cannot breathe. Mars's average temperature is very cold, -60°C.

For all these reasons, Mars is now a cold desert planet with no sign of life on its surface. But was it once a wet, warm world where things lived?

Probes sent to Mars have found signs that it was a very different place in the past. So, astronomers would really like to know if they could change Mars so it became a planet like the Earth, where we could live, breathe and grow food. Changing a planet like this is called "terraforming".

For terraforming to happen, the atmosphere would have to be denser and the temperature hotter. We would have to add greenhouse gases to the atmosphere to catch and hold in the energy from the Sun.

The atmosphere on Mars has only 1% of the pressure of the Earth's atmosphere, which means its gravity is much lower. This means that it might not be possible to keep the atmosphere thick enough for us to breathe and live in. However, scientists think that the pressure in the atmosphere was higher on Mars in the past, so perhaps it could be again. Astronomers know this because they can see where water used to flow on the planet. But liquid water cannot flow on Mars now because any water would turn to gas. People would need water to be able to live there, so astronomers hope that we might be able to use the ice they have found in the north and south of the planet.

Scientists also think that we could use Mars's natural metals and **minerals**. These metals and minerals were brought to the planet's surface when its volcanoes erupted.

There are a lot of reasons why the red planet could be somewhere to live in the future. But it would be a difficult job for the first astronauts landing on Mars. Before they could think about living and growing things on Mars, they would have to find a way of just staying alive there. So, it will take some very brave and clever people to build a new place to live on Mars.

### Jupiter

Jupiter is the fifth planet from the Sun, at an average distance of 778.3 million kilometres. It orbits the Sun once every 11.86 Earth-years. It measures 142,984 kilometres in diameter and, with Saturn, it is one of the two gas **giants**.

For a big planet, it has quite a small core of rock inside, with a layer of liquid metal around it. This layer of liquid becomes an atmosphere of gas around the planet. The famous Great Red Spot, a big red area that you can see on the surface of Jupiter, is actually a huge storm twice the size of the Earth. We know that this storm has lasted for hundreds of years, because it was first seen in 1655, but maybe it actually started earlier than that. The winds on Jupiter can often reach 1,000 kilometres per hour.

So far, astronomers have found seventy-nine moons around Jupiter. We have already read about the four big Galilean moons: Io, Europa, Ganymede and Callisto. They were first seen by Galileo through his telescope in 1610, and they are all about the same size as our Moon.

Europa is only a little bit smaller than our Moon, but it has a much smoother surface, and it does not seem to have any mountains or craters. However, there are dark marks on Europa's crust, which perhaps were formed by warm ice erupting on the planet in the past.

There is probably a big ocean under Europa's thick crust of ice. Astronomers think that this ocean could be 100 kilometres deep. This is much deeper than the deepest part of the ocean on the Earth, the Marianas Trench in the Pacific Ocean, which is about 11 kilometres deep.

Europa's ocean could have some form of life in it. But we do not know if we would find fish swimming in it if we could land on Europa and make a deep hole through several kilometres of ice. Any life found there would probably be more like **microbes** than fish. We should learn more about Europa in the next 10 years, after the JUICE spaceship takes off in 2022. But you will have to be patient, as it will take around 8 years to reach Jupiter, arriving in 2030, before spending 3 years looking at Jupiter, Callisto, Ganymede and Europa.

## Saturn

Saturn is the sixth closest planet to the Sun, at an average distance of 1,430 million kilometres. Saturn orbits the Sun once in every 29.46 Earth-years. It measures 120,536 kilometres at its diameter. It is the second gas giant in the Solar System, made of a hot core of rocks with a layer of liquid metal around it, and another layer of liquid gas around that. There is also an atmosphere around the planet and some amazing rings.

These rings are mostly made of ice with a little bit of rock dust. There are two theories about them. One is that they came from a moon that Saturn used to have. Another is that they came from what was left when Saturn was formed. Jupiter, Uranus and Neptune also have rings, but they do not have as many, and they cannot be seen as easily.

As on Jupiter, the winds in Saturn's atmosphere are very fast, up to 1,795 kilometres per hour. The strongest wind ever recorded on the Earth was 400 kilometres per hour, off the coast of Western Australia in 1996.

So far, astronomers have found eighty-two moons orbiting Saturn, and seven of these are round. Saturn's biggest moon, Titan, is the only known moon in the Solar System to have an atmosphere. Titan is bigger than the planet Mercury and more than three times bigger than our Moon.

Titan was discovered on 25th March 1655 by Dutch astronomer Christiaan Huygens. Coming so soon after Galileo discovered four of Jupiter's moons, this showed

17th-century astronomers that not everything in the Solar System orbited the Earth as they had thought.

Titan takes 15 days and 22 hours to orbit Saturn, the same time as it takes for this moon to turn once on its own axis. So a year on Titan is as long as a day!

Titan's dense atmosphere is formed of gas, which may be like the Earth's atmosphere used to be. But Titan is very cold, and it does not have any carbon dioxide, so life probably cannot start there at the moment. However, Titan might help astronomers understand what the Earth was like a long time ago and how life began on the Earth.

Titan is also as far as a space probe has travelled and landed up until now. On 1st July 2004, the Cassini-Huygens probe reached Saturn. It flew by Titan on 26th October 2004, and the Huygens probe was released from the Cassini probe and landed on Titan on 14th January 2005. Huygens took photographs of Titan's surface and discovered that it rains there. The probe also saw signs that liquid had flowed on Titan in the past. So, in billions of years when our Sun becomes hotter, Titan might become warm enough for life to begin.

Through a telescope, Enceladus looks like a very small white point orbiting Saturn. It is in the densest part of Saturn's rings. It is not one of Saturn's biggest moons, nor one of the easiest to see in the night sky, but astronomers think that Enceladus may be one of the best places to find life in our Solar System. This is because it seems to have liquid water, one of the most important things we need for life. Although the moon was discovered back in 1789 by the astronomer William Herschel, nobody knew very much about it until two Voyager probes passed it in the early 1980s. Voyager 2 found some very old craters and some signs of present activity from volcanoes. Volcanoes on Enceladus are different from those on the Earth. They shoot ice, not lava, into the atmosphere. Some of the ice comes back down to the surface as snow.

The Cassini space probe, which studied Saturn and the moons and rings around it for 13 years, has taken many photos of the ice shooting out from Enceladus. So, if you visited Enceladus, you could build a real snowman in space!

As well as liquid water, Enceladus also has other elements needed for life, which makes it a very special place.

**Uranus**

Uranus is the seventh planet from the Sun, and it is at an average distance of 2,871 million kilometres. It measures 50,800 kilometres in diameter, so it is quite big. It is one of the two planets called "ice giants" – the other is Neptune. It turns on its axis once every 17 hours, 14 minutes, and it looks like it is actually lying on its side. Uranus, like Venus, turns on its axis in the opposite direction to the other planets. Uranus orbits the Sun once every 84 Earth-years. It has the coldest atmosphere of any planet in the Solar System, and an average surface temperature of -197.2°C. It, too, has high winds of up to 900 kilometres per hour.

Uranus was known to astronomers in the past, but they

thought it was a star. Then, in 1781, astronomer William Herschel recorded and described it – at first, he thought it was a comet!

In 1986, the space probe Voyager 2 flew by Uranus and took photographs of it, which showed a blue-green planet with no marks at all on it. Astronomers think it might have a small core made of rock at the centre, a thick layer of ice and gas around it, and another layer of gas atmosphere outside that. Astronomers have found twenty-seven moons so far and at least thirteen dark rings that cannot be seen from the Earth.

## Neptune

Neptune is the eighth planet from the Sun, at an average distance of 4,486 million kilometres. It measures 48,600 kilometres in diameter, and its average surface temperature is -201°C. It turns on its axis once every 18 to 20 hours, and it orbits the Sun once in 164.8 Earth-years.

In many ways, Neptune is very like Uranus. It is also an ice giant, and scientists think it, too, has a small core of rocks, with ice and gas around it. Although the atmosphere is mostly made of hydrogen and a little helium, it looks blue because of the small amount of another gas called methane $(CH_4)$ in its atmosphere.

Astronomers have learned lots of information about Neptune. The information came from the Voyager 2 mission in 1989, the Hubble Space Telescope, and some very powerful telescopes used from the Earth, too. Some of this information is about Neptune's weather. It has a Great Dark Spot, which is an enormous storm, and a Small Dark Spot, which is another storm. It also has something called the "Scooter" – a storm formed of a group of white clouds moving very quickly. Winds on Neptune have also been measured at 2,200 kilometres per hour, which is almost supersonic – faster than the speed of sound. And these winds mostly blow in the opposite direction to the way that the planet turns on its axis.

Astronomers have found fourteen moons around Neptune, and four rings, which are not easy to see.

## CHAPTER SIX

# Dark things

Today, we know that there is a lot more out there in the Universe than just our Solar System. There are billions of galaxies, each made of billions of stars and planets. So, what is the Universe made of?

While our Solar System and other stars and planets are made of atoms, most things in the Universe are not. The Universe is made of strange things called dark matter and dark energy. And we do not yet understand these as well as we understand atoms.

Atoms form about 5% of all the things in the whole Universe. Only about one in ten of those atoms is found in the form of stars, planets or living things. The other atoms are probably still in the form of gases, too hot to form stars or planets.

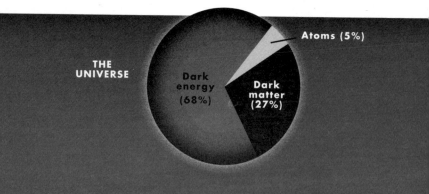

What the Universe is made of

Dark matter makes up about 27% of the rest of the Universe, while dark energy forms the other 68% of it.

At the moment, there are almost more questions than answers about dark matter. We know it is there because the force of its gravity holds together our Galaxy, the Andromeda Galaxy, and all the other big things we can see in the Universe. These galaxies are in the middle of an enormous area of dark matter, ten times bigger than all the galaxies together. Astronomers call this area the "dark halo".

Without the gravity of the dark matter, most of the stars, solar systems, and everything else in the galaxies would go flying off into space.

At the moment, we do not really know what dark matter is made of, but there are some things we do know about it. Dark matter probably does not have the same **particles** that we find in atoms; it is a new form of matter. This should be no surprise as it took nearly 200 years to find all the different kinds of atom.

Astronomers also think that dark matter particles do not feel or notice the particles in atoms or in other dark matter either. So, while the atoms hit each other, fell into the centre of the dark halo and finally formed stars, planets and galaxies, the dark matter stayed where it was. That is why living things are mostly formed from the atoms we know about today and not dark matter.

Dark matter particles move around quickly in the same areas of the Universe as ordinary matter. Astronomers think that at any time there could be about one dark matter particle in every teacup-sized area of the Universe. This means that they may also leave signs behind them that they have been there. These signs could be found by special machines called particle detectors.

Scientists are trying to see whether or not the halo, where our Galaxy sits in space, is formed of dark matter particles. To do this they have put particle detectors under the ground. They work better underground because other particles cannot get there. In Switzerland, scientists have built the Large Hadron Collider, which not only looks for dark matter particles but tries to make them, too.

Satellites in the sky are also looking for pieces of atoms that are formed when dark matter particles in the halo sometimes hit each other and form ordinary matter. This is the opposite to what the Large Hadron Collider is trying to do.

If either of these processes works, we will be sure that something other than atoms makes up most of the matter in the Universe.

As well as dark matter, we also think that there is something in the universe called dark energy, which is trying to do the opposite to dark matter. Dark matter is trying to pull the universe together using gravity, but dark energy is trying to push things away from other things. But how does dark energy do this, and what is it?

We know that the Universe is expanding, having grown in size for the past 13.8 billion years, since the Big Bang.

And since Edwin Hubble discovered this more than 80 years ago, astronomers have been trying to measure how much this process has become slower because of gravity.

Remember that gravity is the force that holds us to the Earth, keeps the planets orbiting the Sun, and holds the Universe together. Gravity pulls objects together and slows down everything that is launched from the Earth, from balls to rockets. So, in the same way, the Universe should be expanding more slowly because of all the things that are attracting each other and slowing them down in the process.

But, in 1998, astronomers discovered that this idea was completely wrong. They did this by using very powerful telescopes like the Hubble Space Telescope to time-travel. Light takes time to travel across the Universe to us, so when we look at things far away, we see them as they were a long time ago and not as they are now. This is how astronomers discovered that the Universe was actually expanding more quickly now than in the past.

According to Einstein's general theory of relativity, there may be "repulsive gravity" in the universe. This means that, instead of pulling things together, repulsive gravity pushes things away from other things. This is called dark energy. It might be caused by the energy from empty space. Or it might be caused by other space–time **dimensions**. Or there may be no dark energy at all, making Einstein's theory of general relativity wrong! That means we would need to find a new theory.

Although we still do not really understand dark energy and how it works, we know that we need to understand it if we want to explain why the Universe is expanding so quickly. If this process continues, in about 100 billion years the whole Universe could become totally dark again. This is because, if we are still here, our nearest star would be so far away that its light would not reach us. Light from other stars would not reach us either, so our universe would look dark!

Or, if our theories are not correct, dark energy which pushes things away might become less than the gravity of dark matter which pulls things together. Then the Universe could suddenly stop expanding, and it might collapse instead. We just do not know!

These are the things that scientists of the future will have to understand and find answers to.

———

A black hole is an area where gravity is so powerful that any light that tries to escape gets pulled back into it. Because nothing can travel faster than light, everything will get pulled in, not just light.

So, if you fell into a black hole, you would never get back out again.

The edge of a black hole is called the "horizon". It is like being on the edge of a waterfall, which has lots of water flowing downhill quickly. If you were above the edge of the waterfall, you could probably get out of the water by swimming fast enough. But once you passed the edge, you would not be able to get out again.

As more things fall into a black hole, it gets bigger and the horizon moves further away. To form a black hole, you need to push a large amount of matter into a very small space. Then, the pull of gravity will be so powerful that light will be pulled back in, and it will not be able to escape. Astronomers think that one way a black hole is formed is when a supernova explodes. Supernovas work like giant bombs: the outside layers of the star are pushed out as gas, and the middle layers are pushed in. If the star is big enough, at least three times the size of the Sun, a black hole will form.

Much bigger black holes are formed at the centre of galaxies, or inside groups of stars. If a black hole meets other things in the Universe, it will make a bigger black hole that pulls everything that gets too close into it. Our Galaxy, the Milky Way, has a black hole several million times the mass of our Sun at its centre.

Finding a black hole used to be like looking for a black cat in the dark. Astronomers could not see them, and they only knew where the black hole was by the way its gravity pulled on the things around it. For example, they knew there was a black hole if they saw stars orbiting something that they could not see, or if gas and dust turned around a central thing that they could not see.

Then, in April 2019, eight telescopes working together on the Earth, called the Event Horizon Telescope, took the first photograph of a black hole. This black hole was found at the core of the enormous galaxy Messier 87. The photograph looks a bit like a ring of light, which is not very clear, with everything behind it black.

As we have already said, you could fall into a black hole, just as you could fall into the Sun. If you fell feet first, your feet would be nearer to the black hole than your head, and they would be pulled harder by the gravity of the black hole. So, you would be pulled into a very long, thin shape. The smaller the black hole, the more you would be pulled. If you fell into a black hole made by a star only a few times the size of our Sun, you would become very long and thin before you reached the black hole! But if you fell into a much bigger black hole, you would pass the horizon, or the edge of the black hole, without noticing anything special.

However, someone watching you fall into the black hole from a distance would not see you cross the horizon. This is because gravity changes time and space near a black hole. To them, you would appear to slow down as you got closer to the edge, and they would not see you as clearly. This is because the light you sent out would take longer and longer to get away from the black hole.

If you crossed the horizon at 11:00 according to your watch, someone watching you would see your watch slow down and never quite reach 11:00.

People used to think that nothing could get out of a black hole once it was in it. Anything that fell into a black hole was thought to be lost and gone forever. A black hole was like a prison you could never escape from.

Then, astronomers discovered that this idea of a black hole was not quite right. Little changes in space and time meant that black holes were not quite the prisons they had imagined them to be. They discovered that particles could escape from black holes in the form of "Hawking Radiation".

Named after Stephen Hawking, one of the writers of this book, Hawking Radiation causes black holes to turn into gas very slowly. The smaller the black hole, the quicker it would become gas. Finally, after billions and billions of years, the black hole would disappear.

But what about the things that had made the black hole, or had fallen into it later? What would happen to them? They would become energy and particles. And, if you looked very carefully at the energy and particles, you would be able to rebuild what had been inside the black hole. So, in a way, you can get out of a black hole!

# CHAPTER SEVEN
## Time travel

Imagine you are a very small **insect**, and you live on the surface of an apple. You cannot easily move around to the other side of the apple, or go anywhere that is not on the apple, so the surface of the apple is your whole universe. Now, imagine that a **worm** has eaten a hole through the middle of the apple. Now, you can get from one side of the apple to the other in two ways: round the apple's surface (your universe); or the second, shorter way through the wormhole.

Scientists want to know if our Universe could be like this apple. Could there be wormholes that can take us from one place in our Universe to another? And, if so, what would these wormholes look like?

The wormhole could have two mouths – one at each end of it. One mouth could maybe be in the middle of London, and the other on a beach in California. The mouths might be round, so you could see everything clearly through them, like a glass ball. But they would not be solid, so you could also walk through them from one place to the other.

The surface of the apple has only two dimensions, and the inside of the apple has three dimensions. The insect could move from the surface of the apple, which has two dimensions, through the inside of the apple, which has three dimensions. In the same way, a wormhole would take you from London in our Universe with three dimensions, through a tunnel or wormhole with four (or more) dimensions that is not part of our Universe, to California (another place in our Universe).

This is possible according to the laws of physics, but it is just a theory for now. And the same theory says that most wormholes would collapse so quickly that nobody could get to the other side alive.

To stop the wormhole from collapsing, we would have to put some special matter into it. This matter would have to make energy that works against gravity to hold the wormhole open. Is this possible? Again, yes, according to the theory!

But, for now, it is probably not possible to find or make enough of this matter to hold the wormhole open long enough for someone to pass through to another part of the Universe.

But what if one day it were possible? You could take a journey that would normally take several years in just a few days. You could even use wormholes to travel back in time and talk to yourself when you were younger. You could change history, or maybe you could not. Stephen Hawking said that the laws of physics made it impossible for anybody to make a time machine and go back and change history. But this, too, is just a theory for now.

We all know about time, or at least we think we do. And we all know the *tick tock* sound a clock makes as time passes. When we are together in a room, my clock shows the same time as your clock, and time passes in the same way. If you went on holiday somewhere far away, our clocks would show a different time of day, but your *tick tock* and mine would still be the same.

But we saw in Chapter Two that time is interesting because it can pass differently if you start to move very fast. When you measure the *tick tock* on a spaceship going very fast into space, it looks slower than the *tick tock* of a clock back on the Earth. Scientists call this "time dilation", and it happens because light can only go at a speed (called "c" in physics) around 300,000 kilometres per second, and no faster. Although light can slow down when it passes through something thick like glass, when it travels in free space, its speed is "c" in any direction that you shine the light in.

So, time on a super-fast-moving spaceship passes more slowly than time on the Earth. This is the theory that explains how someone can travel one way into the future – travelling so fast that only days pass, while on the Earth years go by. It seems hard to believe, but that is because it is impossible for us to move fast enough to notice.

## CHAPTER EIGHT
# Satellites and why we need them

A satellite is an object that orbits another thing, like the Moon around the Earth. The Earth is a satellite of the Sun. However, we also use the word "satellite" to mean the artificial things that are sent into space on rockets, which help us find our way, talk to each other or check the weather.

The Chinese made the first rockets about a thousand years ago. Many hundreds of years later, on 4th October 1957, the Russians used a rocket to launch the first satellite into orbit around the Earth. The Russians called it Sputnik, but some people called it the "Red Moon", and from all around the world they listened to the messages it sent back to the Earth. The Mark I telescope at Jodrell Bank Observatory in the UK was the first large radio telescope to be used to follow the satellite.

Sputnik II was launched later the same year. It was also known as "Pupnik" because it was the first satellite to carry a living animal into orbit – a Russian dog called Laika.

On 6th December 1957, the Americans tried to launch their own satellite, but it only got 1.2 metres off the ground before the rocket exploded. They finally succeeded in launching Explorer I into space on 1st February 1958. After that, the Russians and the Americans were in a competition to be the greatest country in space.

The USA and Russia did not really trust each other, and they soon realized that satellites were good for secretly watching people. They tried to learn more about what was happening in each other's countries by taking photographs from above the Earth.

Satellite technology was originally developed for the army. In the 1970s, the USA launched twenty-four satellites, which sent back time signals and information about orbits. Thanks to this, the first global positioning system, or "GPS", was developed. GPS allows armies to cross deserts by night, and ordinary people not to get lost! The technology it uses is known as satellite navigation or "satnav". It also helps ambulances to reach people who are hurt or ill more quickly, and to find people who are lost at sea.

Satellites are also good for allowing people to contact each other across the world. In 1962, a US telephone company launched Telstar, a satellite that sent out the first-ever television show from the USA to Britain and France in real time. The British only saw a few minutes of pictures, and they were not very clear, but the French had both clear pictures and sound.

After Telstar, big world events like the football World Cup in 1966 could be seen across the world in real time. Today, we use satellite technology with our mobile phones and the internet.

---

Satellite cameras are not only used to secretly watch people. They can study the atmosphere, measure land use, see cities expanding and deserts and forests changing shape. Satellite pictures can also be used to check how plants are growing on farms.

Satellites help us to understand the weather, too. They may not be able to change the weather, but they can correctly tell us what weather is coming and how it may change in the future. This gives us time to get to a safe place when bad weather is coming.

At the end of the 1990s, the National Aeronautics and Space Administration (NASA) satellite TOPEX/Poseidon, in the USA, helped people to understand the "El Niño" event. This is when the surface of the Pacific Ocean gets warmer every few years, affecting the world's **climate**.

NASA also launched Jason, a group of satellites that study how the ocean affects climate change on the Earth. The satellites give information about ice melting, seas disappearing, and the water rising in oceans.

Just as satellites look back at the Earth and help us to understand our planet, they have also changed the way we see the Universe around us. The Hubble Space Telescope was the first really big space observatory orbiting the Earth. It has helped astronomers learn the age of the Universe and shown that it is expanding more quickly.

---

A space probe is a robot spaceship, without any people on it, that scientists send across the Solar System to find information about the Universe. These probes try to answer questions like: "What does the surface of Venus look like?" or "Is it windy on Neptune?" or "What is Jupiter made of?"

Many people get less excited about probes than they do about people going into space. But it is often better to send probes than people for several reasons.

Probes can travel greater distances and travel faster than any astronaut can. Space probes do not need as much energy to fly as spaceships with people on them. And they do not have to be as big or as comfortable because they do not need to carry food, water or oxygen for astronauts to breathe. Robots do not feel bored, alone or get ill like people. It costs less to send probes into space, because they do not want to come back home again. And, importantly, nobody dies if there is a problem on a probe.

There are different types of space probe according to their use. Some probes fly past planets and take pictures, some orbit a planet to learn more about that planet and its moons, and others are made to land and send back information from the surface of another planet. Some of these probes are rovers, which means they move around after they land, while others stay in the place where they land.

Space probes have shown us new parts of the Solar System, sending back information that has allowed scientists to understand how the Solar System was formed and what it is like on other planets. Astronauts have only travelled as far as the Moon so far, a journey of around 378,000 kilometres. But probes have travelled billions of kilometres and shown us amazing pictures from the most distant parts of the Solar System.

Probes have caught the dust from a comet's tail, they have landed on Mars and on Venus, and travelled past Pluto. Some probes have taken information about our planet and its people with them. Probes Pioneer 10 and 11 carry pictures of a man and a woman, and a map showing where the probe came from, ready for any aliens out there to find one day. The Voyager probes carry photographs of cities, the natural world and people on the Earth, as well as recorded messages in different Earth languages. Because of these things, if aliens ever find them, they will know that the Earth is a planet of peace, and that its people do not want to hurt them.

The first rover, Lunokhod 1 (part of Russian probe Luna 17), was controlled from the Earth when it landed on the Moon in 1970.

Many probes have failed to land on Mars because it is not easy to do. But NASA's Viking 1 and Viking 2 landed on Mars in 1976, and gave us our first pictures from the surface of the red planet. They showed red-brown plains, with rocks and a pink sky. Later, Mars rovers Spirit and Opportunity, which were supposed to be able to drive around for at least 3 months but lasted much longer than that, found signs of water on Mars from its past.

In 2007, NASA sent the Phoenix probe to Mars. It could not drive around, but it had a long robot arm to make a hole in the ground and collect bits of dirt and rocks. Phoenix was also able to look and see what was just under the surface, while still on Mars. There have since been several more satellites orbiting and probes landing on Mars, helping us to learn about its surface and atmosphere.

Space probes have also shown us what is below the thick atmosphere of Venus. Once, it was thought that dense, hot forests might lie under Venus's clouds. But space probes have found a hot and heavy atmosphere of gas and liquid there. NASA's Magellan probe entered orbit around Venus in 1990 and found 167 volcanoes larger than 110 kilometres wide on the surface of Venus. And several Russian probes have actually landed on Venus, which is very difficult to do, and sent back new information, too.

Probes have also visited Mercury, which is closer to the Sun than Venus. Mariner 10, which flew by Mercury in 1974 and 1975, showed us that it looked a lot like our Moon. It is a grey, dead planet with very little atmosphere. Then, in 2008, the MESSENGER probe flew by Mercury and sent us the first new pictures of the planet for 30 years.

There are a lot of problems for probes flying close to the Sun, because it is so hot. But several space probes, like Helios 1, Helios 2, SOHO, TRACE and RHESSI, have succeeded in sending back information from the Sun itself. And this has helped scientists to better understand the whole Solar System. DSCOVR is studying the winds and

**Curiosity Mars rover**

other things released by the Sun at the moment. And the Parker Solar Probe is going to try to get as close as it can to the Sun in 2025.

Far out in the Solar System, Jupiter was first seen close up when the probe Pioneer 10 flew by in 1973, showing us the Great Red Spot. The Voyager probes discovered that Jupiter's moons were all very different from each other. And we have already learned how the Galileo probe studied Jupiter and its moons for 8 years, giving us a lot of new information.

NASA's Cassini probe was not the first to visit Saturn. Pioneer 11 and the Voyager probes had flown past on their long journeys and sent back amazing pictures of Saturn's rings and information about the thick atmosphere on its moon Titan. But when Cassini arrived in 2004, it gave us more information about the moons that orbit Saturn.

And its Huygens probe discovered the ice and rain on Titan.

After a longer journey, the probe Voyager 2 flew by Uranus and brought us pictures of the ice planet lying on its side. Thanks to this probe, we also know much more about the thin rings around Uranus and more information about its moons.

Voyager 2 continued travelling to Neptune and showed us the fastest-moving winds in the Solar System. At the end of 2019, Voyager 2 was about 18 billion kilometres from the Earth, and Voyager 1 was around 22 billion kilometres away. We hope that they will continue to send back pictures and information to the Earth.

## CHAPTER NINE
# Why people go into space

Russian astronaut Yuri Gagarin was the first human in space. He orbited the Earth on 12th April 1961 in the spacecraft Vostok I. Six weeks later, US President John F. Kennedy said that he wanted to land a man on the Moon in less than 10 years. So, the newly-formed NASA started working to send astronauts into space. At that time, NASA had only 16 minutes' experience of flying in space, but now the race to be the first on the Moon had begun!

In 1961, astronaut Alan Shepard became the first American in space, flying for 15 minutes, without quite orbiting the Earth. The year after, John Glenn became the first NASA astronaut to orbit the Earth. NASA's Project Gemini followed, teaching astronauts how to bring two spaceships together. Astronauts also learned how to walk in space, although the first-ever spacewalk was done in 1965 by Russian astronaut Alexei Leonov.

However, the Americans reached the Moon before the Russians. "The Eagle has landed!" was the message that US astronaut Neil Armstrong sent by radio from the Moon to the Earth on 20th July 1969.

But this eagle (a large, wild bird) was not actually a bird; it was the part of the spaceship that had taken astronauts Neil Armstrong and Buzz Aldrin on to the Moon, while Michael Collins orbited the Moon in the spaceship.

**American astronauts landing on the Moon**

Armstrong was the first person to step on to the Moon.
Aldrin followed him and looked around at the totally black
sky, the impact craters and the layers of dust. They quickly
put rocks and dust into their pockets to take with them if
they had to leave suddenly. But they stayed on the Moon
for almost a day, walking a kilometre on foot. This journey
was one of the most important in human history. And
three craters on the Moon are named after the astronauts:
Aldrin, Armstrong and Collins.

A total of twelve astronauts have walked on the Moon. Each time it was very dangerous for the carefully trained astronauts, who had to work very hard with the tens of thousands of people who build and manage the spaceships back on the Earth. Astronauts have brought back 381 kilograms of rocks and dust from the Moon, to be studied on the Earth. This has allowed scientists to better understand the Moon and how it affects the Earth.

After the race to be the first to land on the Moon ended, many people became less interested in space. However, both the Russians and the Americans still had big plans. The Russians were working secretly on something called Almaz, which means "diamond". They wanted to have a space station, a place where people could live while orbiting the Earth. They sent several space stations into space, but none lasted much more than a year.

The Americans developed their own space station, Skylab, which lasted for 8 months in 1973. Skylab had a telescope on board that astronauts used to look at the Sun, and they brought back special photographs. They were photographs taken of the inside of the Sun, showing solar flares. These happen when parts of the Sun suddenly get very bright. There were also photographs of dark spots. These are parts of the Sun's surface that appear darker and not as hot.

On the Earth in the 1970s, Russia and the USA were in the Cold War. This meant that they were not actually fighting, but they did not like or trust each other.

However, in space, the two countries began working together. In 1975, Apollo, a US spaceship, attached itself to Soyuz, a Russian one. The American astronauts and the Russian astronauts shook hands with each other in space.

The space shuttle was a new type of spaceship. You could fly it into space like a rocket, but bring it back down to the Earth again and land it like an aeroplane. Then it could fly back into space again and again. It could carry things, as well as astronauts, into space. Enterprise was the first shuttle. It was used for testing, but it could not orbit the Earth. The first US shuttle to fly in space was Columbia, launched in 1981. And the last shuttle to fly was Atlantis, in July 2011.

In 1986, the Russians launched the space station Mir, which means "world" or "peace". It was the first complex, large space station ever to orbit the Earth. It took 10 years to build in space, and you could do experiments on it in an almost gravity-free environment. It was about the size of a London bus, and between three and six astronauts could live in it together.

Astronauts started building the International Space Station (ISS) in space in 1998. It orbits the Earth every 90 minutes and is a place where astronauts, and astronomers back on the Earth, from many countries work together. NASA's space shuttle, the Russian spaceship Soyuz, and Automated Transfer Vehicles belonging to the European Space Agency (ESA) were used to take people and things to and from the ISS. Now, Russian and European rockets fly there, as well as small SpaceX and Crew Dragon spaceships called capsules. The astronauts also have a way of escaping the ISS in an emergency!

———————

But why use all that energy and do all that work, just for a bit of the Moon? Aren't there better things we could be doing here on the Earth?

If we could move into space, it would totally change the future for humans. It could even decide whether or not we have a future at all. It will not give us the answers to the problems we have on the Earth right now, but it will help us look at them in a different way. The time has come when we need to look outwards across the Universe instead of in at ourselves on this very full planet.

But we will not be able to move people into space quickly. It could take hundreds or even thousands of years. We could start by having somewhere to stay on the Moon in 30 years, reach Mars in 50 years, and explore the moons of the planets far away from the Sun in 200 years.

Reaching and exploring other planets would mean astronauts flying there, not just robots as has happened in the past. But we are not yet sure where we can live. Astronauts have lived for months on the ISS, so we know they can live away from the Earth. But we also know that living without gravity for a long time is not very healthy. If we are to live in space for longer, it has to be on a planet or a moon.

We could choose to go to the Moon first because it is

close, easy to get to, and we have been there before. But it is small, it has no atmosphere and there is no liquid water on it. So, maybe the Moon could just be where we start our journey into the Solar System.

What about Mars? It is the next planet after the Earth and not too close to the Sun. But, again, there is no real atmosphere or pressure any more, and the water is in ice form. Could we use this to live?

NASA astronomers think that, in the summer months, water on Mars flows down craters, before disappearing when the temperature falls in the autumn. But we do not understand where this water comes from yet. It could come from under the ground or from the atmosphere on Mars.

But it would take about 200 days to get to Mars, without stopping on the way. It would be too far for extra food or water to be sent to astronauts. There would be no phone calls home, and even an email could take more than 20 minutes to reach them. There would be no TV to stop them from getting bored. Only recorded books, films and TV shows.

Every day, they would have to cook, clean, grow food, look after the spaceship, record videos for students back home, and do experiments inside and outside the spaceship. They would have to wear a spacesuit to breathe outside the spaceship, and washing would be difficult, because there would be so little water. They would miss friends, family, favourite foods, warm showers and fresh air. So, could we really travel to and live on Mars?

Mercury and Venus are too hot to live on, while Jupiter and Saturn are gas giants, so they do not have a solid surface to live on. As for Uranus or Neptune, they are just too cold and too far away, and you could not live on them because, like Jupiter and Saturn, they have no solid surfaces.

We could try the moons of Mars, but they are very small. Some of the moons of Jupiter and Saturn might be better. For example, Saturn's moon Titan is larger than our Moon and has a dense atmosphere, so that is a possible place. But we know it is very cold because it is so far from the Sun, and it has liquid gas on it – so maybe it is not possible!

What about places outside our Solar System? There are quite a few planets the size of Jupiter or Saturn. But now we have found some smaller Earth-like planets, too, which lie in the Goldilocks Zone of their star systems. They could have water on their surfaces. There are maybe a thousand stars nearer than 10 light years to the Earth. If just 1% of these have an Earth-sized planet in the Goldilocks Zone, there are ten possible new worlds out there! But, for now, we cannot travel very far across the Universe. We cannot imagine how we could travel so far. But that is what we could try to do in the next 200 to 500 years.

———

Once you get there, what is it actually like in space? Almost everyone dreams of going into space at some point in their lives. Sadly, most people stop dreaming about it when they discover how hard it is to do. But more people can do it now than in the past, thanks to private companies that are flying people into space and to the ISS.

It is hard work getting ready to go into space. You have to learn how to fly a spaceship, about air pressure and gases in space, and how to use a radio on a spaceship.

When the spaceship finally takes off, it is not as loud as you might imagine. For about 8 minutes, you feel about three times the force of gravity, before the engines turn off. Then you are moving in zero-gravity in the orbit around the Earth. If you are flying to the ISS, you actually stay quite close to the Earth, and you can see the Earth below you if you look out of the window. At the same time, you are near to the Earth, but in a totally different world from the people on its surface. You and the other people on board the spaceship must immediately manage any emergency. So, you have to work well alone and as part of a group, with very little help from the Earth.

When orbiting the Earth on the ISS, you are travelling at 27,690 kilometres per hour. So, you go all the way around our planet about every 90 minutes. That means you see the Sun rise and go down every 45 minutes, and you cross countries very quickly. But you are still close enough to the Earth to see famous things like the Golden Gate Bridge in San Francisco.

One of the first things you notice about the Earth from space is its weather. A lot of the Earth is always covered by clouds. The next thing you notice is how beautiful the deserts of the Earth are, as they are not usually covered by clouds. And you can see how the winds affect sand and snow on the Earth.

It is also clear that humans live on the whole surface of the Earth. There are hardly any empty spaces left on it. Every desert has roads across it, and often there are farms in deserts, too, getting water from under the ground. Every forest has roads and cities in it – in the Amazon forest, too. Every group of mountains has roads through it, and rivers have walls to control where they flow.

It is a bit like watching a film, which makes you realize just how small and in danger the Earth really is. Many astronauts have this feeling when they see the Earth from space. The experience changes them. It is called the "Overview Effect".

## CHAPTER TEN

# Big questions about the Universe

### Will we ever meet aliens?

The distances in space are so great that we cannot be sure that we will ever meet an alien in person. But, even if we do not, we might still be able to contact one by radio.

Radio waves can move through the empty spaces between stars in a way that sound waves cannot. And they can move as fast as anything can move, at the speed of light. Almost 50 years ago, some scientists discovered that a conversation between different planets would not need very complex technology. Just as we can send messages with the type of radios we can already build, aliens probably can, too. So, the scientists started trying to listen for radio messages from aliens, but so far they have not found any.

### If we cannot hear aliens, perhaps they aren't there?

Let's hope not, as that would mean that we are not only very special, but also very alone in the Universe. Some scientists prefer to believe that, so far, we have not been looking or listening for radio messages in the right place, or at the right time. And, luckily, new radio telescopes are making this search for radio messages easier to do.

### What might aliens say to us?

We can only really guess, but let's hope that they would send a long message. Fast conversations between different planets are impossible. If an alien sent us a message from an exoplanet 1,000 light years away, it would take 1,000 years to reach us. It would not really matter that it was an old message, it would still be interesting, but the aliens would have to wait another 1,000 years for us to get our answer back to them. So, it might be a better idea for aliens to send whole books with information about themselves and their planet.

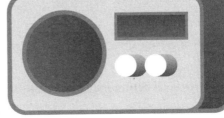

**Listening for a radio message from aliens**

### Could we understand an alien's message?

The messages would not be in English or any other Earth language, but they might have pictures or maths to help us understand them. It does not even matter what the message is, and how well we understand it, it would still be amazing to find that humans are not the only ones watching the Universe.

### Will we ever walk on Mars?

Let's hope so! Scientists believe that we probably will. And it will be both a dangerous and an exciting adventure. Through history, humans have explored new countries, crossed deep oceans, reached the North and South Poles, and climbed the highest mountains. Those who travel to Mars will go hoping for the same type of adventure. It would be amazing to cross the mountains and craters of Mars, or fly over them. But nobody would go to Mars for a comfortable life. It will be harder to live there than at the top of Mount Everest or at the South Pole.

### What could we find on Mars?

The greatest hope would be to find something alive on Mars. Here on the Earth there are millions of forms of life. From microbes to plants, to animals, and of course humans. They live in the far corners of our planet: in wet, dark places; dry, hot deserts; around very hot water; underground and high in the atmosphere.

What every living thing can do on the Earth depends on

its shape and size. Big animals have fat legs but still cannot jump like insects. And the largest animals of all live in water. There could be many different types of animal on other planets. If gravity were weaker, animals could be bigger, and the animals our size could have legs as thin as insects'.

## Would we recognize other intelligent life?

We would already know about intelligent life if it were on Mars. And there is not any on Mercury or Venus, as both are too hot. If there were life on Jupiter, where the force of gravity is much more powerful than on the Earth, it would have to be very strange to stay alive in its dense atmosphere.

But there could be living things swimming in the ocean under the ice on Jupiter's moon Europa. NASA would like to visit it, but landing is difficult because of the ice on its surface. Some scientists think that Titan, Saturn's biggest moon, might be a good place for life, but life has not been found there yet.

Even if they were not so far away, we might not recognize intelligent aliens living on exoplanets. Or maybe they just do not want us to know about them if they are watching us.

The truth is that there could be very intelligent animals, having complex ideas, under an alien ocean somewhere in the Universe, or lots of insects working together like one intelligent thing, and we might never know it.

The problem is that we do not know what intelligent life could be like, or even if it is out there at all. Maybe it is only on the Earth, or maybe we just have not found it yet. And if we do find alien life in the future, it could be very different from us.

### What problems could the Earth have from space?

An asteroid could hit the Earth. There are probably millions of asteroids in our Solar System. Some are only a metre across, but others can be hundreds of kilometres in diameter. Sometimes, an asteroid is pushed out of its orbit by the gravity from planets near it, and then it could hit the Earth. About once a year, a rock the size of a family car enters the Earth's atmosphere, but burns up before it reaches the surface. Once every few thousand years, a rock about the size of a playing field hits the Earth. And every few million years, Earth is hit by an asteroid or a comet, and the explosion is big enough to put life on Earth in danger. An asteroid hit the Earth 65 million years ago and killed the dinosaurs – enormous animals that once lived on the planet.

We could also be burned by gamma rays from space. When very big stars explode and die, they send hot dust and gas into the Universe in an expanding cloud. Dangerous gamma rays also shoot out of these stars as very bright light. If the Earth were very near, and directly in the path of a gamma ray, it could cause clouds of brown gas to fill the sky, so we could not breathe. But luckily this does not happen very often, so astronomers are not worried!

### What problems could the Earth have from us?

There are many, many people on the planet – more than

7 billion. This means that we need to grow more food for everyone, and the extra gases this sends into the Earth's atmosphere are making the planet warmer in a process called climate change. If the planet continues warming, some places will get hotter and have no rain, while people living near the coast will have problems caused by the sea rising.

There are also fewer animals and plants on the Earth, as we have moved into the places where they live and grow.

Millions of years ago, before there were humans, there were plants and animals everywhere. When they died, they fell to the ground and were covered by dirt and minerals, carried by wind and water. These layers grew, and, as the temperature and the pressure increased, they finally became fossil fuels. We use these fossil fuels for energy, to bring heat and light to our homes and to drive our cars. But, when we burn them, we release carbon dioxide, which causes the greenhouse effect and climate change.

We know climate change is bad for animals and plants. But it also causes problems for humans, like extremely bad weather; not enough, too much or poor water; natural emergencies; and wars, to name a few of them.

### What are the answers to the Earth's problems?

We should stop using fossil fuels for energy and use cleaner energy from the wind and the Sun, which we can use again and again, and which does not release dangerous greenhouse gases.

We should also stop throwing so much **plastic** into our rubbish. Plastic makes a lot of everyday things, but it is also made using fossil fuels.

We should grow more trees, which use carbon dioxide in their natural processes, helping to lower the greenhouse gases in our atmosphere. Most importantly, we should stop burning or cutting down the trees and forests that we already have on the Earth.

We must also stop throwing rubbish into our oceans, which is making them dirtier and warmer, killing the plants and animals that are living there.

We all need to take time to learn about the causes of climate change and how it will affect our planet in the future. We should try to become a little more like the famous young Swedish schoolgirl Greta Thunberg, who is fighting to save our planet.

In the words of Stephen Hawking, every one of us should "Remember to look up at the stars and not down at your feet."

# During-reading questions

**CHAPTER ONE**

  **1**  What did the Greeks used to believe about the Universe?

  **2**  What is the "Big Bang", and when did it happen?

**CHAPTER TWO**

  **1**  What two things did Sir Isaac Newton develop laws about?

  **2**  What did Albert Einstein discover about the speed of light?

**CHAPTER THREE**

  **1**  How do the Moon and the planets shine at night?

  **2**  What is Pluto, and why is it not a planet?

  **3**  What are exoplanets?

**CHAPTER FOUR**

  **1**  List the things that plants, animals and humans need for life.

  **2**  What is the Goldilocks Zone?

**CHAPTER FIVE**

  **1**  Which planet is the hottest in the Solar System and the closest to Earth?

  **2**  Which planets are the two gas giants of the Solar System?

**CHAPTER SIX**

  **1**  What is the Universe made up of?

  **2**  Before the 2019 Event Horizon Telescope photograph of a black hole, how could you find one?

## CHAPTER SEVEN

1 What could a wormhole be like?
2 What does "time dilation" help us to understand?

## CHAPTER EIGHT

1 How are satellites used to help people today?
2 Why can space probes sometimes be better than spaceships with people on them?

## CHAPTER NINE

1 Who was the first human in space, and how and when did it happen?
2 What is the "Overview Effect"?

## CHAPTER TEN

1 Why would it be important for aliens to send a long message?
2 What problems could the Earth have from space?

---

# After-reading questions

1 What new things have you learned about the Universe?
2 Which astronomer do you think helped us to learn the most about the Universe?
3 How can black holes, dark energy and wormholes help us to understand the Universe?
4 Why do people want to travel into space?
5 Where in the Universe do you think we might find intelligent life, and why?

# Exercises

**1** **Match the words with their definitions in your notebook.**

*Example:* 1 – c

| | | | |
|---|---|---|---|
| **1** | Universe | **a** | a person who studies space |
| **2** | Solar System | **b** | billions of stars, gas and dust, held together by gravity |
| **3** | telescope | **c** | everything around us on the Earth and in space |
| **4** | galaxy | **d** | get bigger |
| **5** | astronomer | **e** | move around a star or a planet in space |
| **6** | orbit | **f** | the force that keeps us on the surface of the Earth |
| **7** | gravity | **g** | the group of eight planets and their moons which go around our Sun |
| **8** | expand | **h** | you can use it to look into space to make things appear closer |

**2** **Write the correct words in your notebook.**

**1** Galileo Galilei was born near Pisa in Italy, *although* / **because** his family came from Florence.

**2** He was studying to be a doctor **after** / **before** he changed to maths and philosophy.

**3** **When** / **While** he was just eighteen, he watched a light high on the ceiling in Pisa Cathedral.

**4** **According to** / **As** the story, Galileo climbed to the top of the tower and dropped stones from it.

**5** Galileo developed a new telescope, **which** / **who** marked the true start of astronomy.

**6** He saw four moons orbiting Jupiter, **but** / **so** he realized that not everything in the Solar System went around the Earth.

**CHAPTERS THREE TO SIX**

**3** **Complete these sentences with the correct verb in your notebook.**

| believe | have | be | be | flow |
|---------|------|----|----|------|

**1** People used to ........*believe*........ that the Moon was a mirror, or a bowl of fire, and that it was magic.

**2** Pluto used to .......... thought of as a planet, but it is now called a dwarf planet.

**3** Astronomers can see where water used to .......... on the planet Mars.

**4** One theory about Saturn's rings is that they came from a moon that the planet used to ...........

**5** Titan's dense atmosphere is formed of gas, which may be like the Earth's atmosphere used to ...........

**4** **Match the two parts of these sentences in your notebook.**

*Example:* 1 – f

1 We should measure our weight in newtons,

2 When you travel across the Solar System,

3 When you land on a planet or moon with weaker gravity than the Earth,

4 If your weight was 34 kilograms on the Earth,

5 You could jump very high on the Moon,

6 Or at least you would

a your weight changes although your mass stays the same.

b but you would find it hard to take just one step on the ground on Jupiter.

c it would be 5.6 kilograms on the Moon.

d if Jupiter had solid ground.

e your mass does not change but your weight does.

f because they describe the force of gravity.

**5** **Complete these sentences in your notebook, using the words from the box.**

| axis | process | liquid | atmosphere | surface |
| --- | --- | --- | --- | --- |
| | microbes | | diameter | |

**1** Mercury turns very slowly on its ............*axis*............; each day lasts 59 Earth-days.

**2** The heat on Venus's surface cannot escape because its atmosphere experiences a ........... called the "greenhouse effect", with gases holding the heat in.

**3** The ........... of Mars is 6,805 kilometres, and it has an iron core.

**4** The famous Great Red Spot, a big red area that you can see on the ........... of Jupiter, is actually a huge storm twice the size of the Earth.

**5** Any life found in Europa's ocean would probably be more like ........... than fish.

**6** Saturn is made of a hot core of rocks with a layer of ........... metal and gas around it.

**7** Uranus has the coldest ........... of any planet in the Solar System, and an average surface temperature of -197.2°C.

**6** **Write the adverb form of these adjectives in your notebook.**

The Universe should be expanding more ¹.........*slowly*.......... (**slow**) because of all the things that are attracting each other and slowing them down in the process. But, in 1998, astronomers discovered that this idea was ²........... (**complete**) wrong. They did this by using very strong telescopes to time-travel. Light takes time to travel across the Universe to us, so when we look at things far away, we see them as they were a long time ago and not as they are now. This is how astronomers discovered that the Universe was ³........... (**actual**) expanding more ⁴........... (**quick**) now than in the past. Although we still do not ⁵........... (**real**) understand dark energy and how it works, we know that we need to understand it.

**7** **Complete these collocations in your notebook, using the verbs from the box.**

| make | launch | find | check | talk | take |

1 .......*make*....... energy/a hole in the ground/a sound
2 .......... photographs/a journey/us from place to place
3 .......... your way/people/some information
4 .......... to aliens/to each other/to yourself
5 .......... the weather/how plants are growing/the time
6 .......... a satellite/a rocket/a probe/a spaceship

## CHAPTER NINE

**8** **Write the correct verb form in your notebook.**

Russian astronaut Yuri Gagarin [1]*orbited* / had orbited / was orbiting the Earth on 12th April 1961 in the spacecraft Vostok I. Six weeks later, US President John F. Kennedy said that he wanted [2]**land** / **landing** / **to land** a man on the Moon in less than 10 years. So, the newly-formed NASA started [3]**to work** / **worked** / **working** to send astronauts into space. At that time, NASA had only 16 minutes' experience of [4]**fly** / **flying** / **to fly** in space, but now the race to be the first on the Moon [5]**began** / **had begun** / **to begin**! On 20th July 1969, the Americans [6]**reached** / **to reach** / **were reaching** the Moon before the Russians.

## CHAPTER TEN

**9** **Write these sentences as reported speech in your notebook.**

**1** The distances in space are so great that we cannot be sure that we will ever meet an alien in person.

*The writer said that the distances in space were so great that we could not be sure that we would ever meet an alien in person.*

**2** We can only really guess what aliens might say to us, but let's hope that they would send a long message.

**3** If we do find alien life in the future, it could be very different from us.

**4** Every few million years, Earth is hit by an asteroid or a comet, and the explosion is big enough to put life on Earth in danger.

**5** There are also fewer animals and plants on the Earth, as we have moved into the places where they live and grow.

**6** We all need to take time to learn about the causes of climate change and how it will affect our planet in the future.

**10** **What happened here? Match the two parts of these sentences in your notebook.**

*Example:* 1 – h

1 The Andromeda Galaxy, the nearest large galaxy to the Milky Way,

2 The "Weird Terrain"

3 Saturn's moon Titan

4 Uranus

5 The Earth

6 The Eagle

7 US spaceship Apollo

8 The International Space Station

a was discovered on 25th March 1655 by Dutch astronomer Christiaan Huygens.

b was first orbited by the satellite Sputnik in 1957.

c was first photographed in 1986 by the spaceship Voyager 2.

d was attached to Russian spaceship Soyuz in space in 1975, and the astronauts shook hands.

e took astronauts Neil Armstrong and Buzz Aldrin to the Moon on 20th July 1969.

f was probably formed on Mercury by the things that hit it in the past.

g was built in space for astronauts and astronomers from many countries to work together.

h was first discovered in 1924 by Edwin Hubble.

# Project work

1  Talk to your friends about one of the big questions in the book:

   - Will we ever meet aliens, and how will we talk to them?
   - Would we recognize other intelligent life if we found it?
   - Will we ever walk on Mars: how and when?
   - What are the Earth's biggest problems, and what can we do about them?

2  Look online, and write an article about Stephen Hawking. Find out:

   **a** where and when he was born

   **b** what and where he studied

   **c** what he discovered and achieved

   **d** why he was such an important scientist.

3  Make a poster to explain one of the theories in the book (wormholes, dark matter and energy, time travel). In your poster, say:

   **a** what it is

   **b** how it works

   **c** why it is important.

An answer key for all questions and exercises can be found at **www.penguinreaders.co.uk**

# Glossary

**artificial** (adj.)
not natural, made by people

**asteroid** (n.)
a large rock that moves
around the Sun

**astronaut** (n.)
An *astronaut* travels into *space*.

**astronomer** (n.)
**astronomy** (n.)
An *astronomer* studies *space*.
*Astronomy* is studying *space*.

**atmosphere** (n.)
all the gases around a *planet*

**atom** (n.)
*Atoms* are very small things that
everything is made of.

**attract** (v.)
when one thing pulls another
thing towards it

**average** (adj.)
An *average* amount is the middle
amount. If you add two or more
numbers together and divide
them by the number of numbers
that you added, you get the
*average* number.

**axis** (n.)
An *axis* goes through the middle
of a *planet*, and the *planet* turns
around it. An *axis* is not real –
people imagine it.

**bubble** (n.)
a ball of gas or air with *liquid*
around it

**cause** (v.)
to make something happen

**(chemical) element** (n.)
something that is made
from only one type of *atom*.
Everything in the world is
made from one or more *chemical
elements*.

**clear** (adj.)
easy to see

**climate** (n.)
what the weather is like in a
place. The weather in the world
is changing. This is called *climate*
change.

**collapse** (v.)
to fall down or towards the
inside

**comet** (n.)
a moving object in *space* that
leaves a bright line behind it in
the sky

**complex** (adj.)
A *complex* thing has a lot of different parts and is difficult to understand.

**dense** (adj.)
1. very heavy
2. thick and difficult to move or see through

**diameter** (n.)
a line that goes through the centre of a circle, from one side to the other side. If a *planet* is 1,000 kilometres in *diameter*, it is 1,000 kilometres long from one side to the other side.

**dimension** (n.)
The *dimensions* of something are how long, wide or high it is.

**distance** (n.)
how far it is between two places or things

**dust** (n.)
very small pieces of rock or dirt

**dwarf planet** (n.)
a large, round piece of rock, metal or gas that moves around the Sun or a *star*

**energy** (n.)
something like gas that makes heat or light or can make things move

**erupt** (v.)
If a *volcano erupts*, it *explodes* inside and throws out fire, smoke and very hot rock or *liquid*.

**expand** (v.)
to become larger

**explode** (v.)
to suddenly break into many pieces

**fizzy** (adj.)
A *fizzy* drink has lots of gas *bubbles* in it.

**flow** (v.)
If a *liquid* flows, it keeps moving along in one direction.

**force** (n.)
strong *energy*. The *force* of *gravity* pulls things towards a *planet*.

**form** (v. and n.)
to make something begin to exist (= be there in the *universe*). The *form* of something is the way in which it exists.

**further** (adv.)
at a place that is a longer *distance* from something than another thing

**galaxy** (n.)
a very large group of *stars* in the *universe*

**giant** (adj. and n.)
extremely big, or much bigger than other things of the same type. A *giant* is an extremely big person or thing.

**gravity** (n.)
*Gravity* is the *force* that pulls things towards a *planet*.

**insect** (n.)
a very small animal with six legs. *Insects* are usually smaller than a finger.

**land** (v.)
to go down to the ground after a journey in a plane or *spaceship*

**launch** (v.)
to send a *satellite* or *spaceship* up into the sky

**layer** (n.)
A *layer* is flat and lies under or on top of another *surface*.

**light year** (n.)
the *distance* that light travels in one year. We use *light years* to *measure distances* in *space*.

**liquid** (n. and adj.)
A *liquid* is a thing like water. It is not *solid* or a gas. *Liquid* is the adjective of *liquid*.

**mass** (n.)
the amount of *matter* that is inside something or someone

**matter** (n.)
the *liquids*, gases and *solid* things that everything in the *universe* is made of

**measure** (v.)
to find the size, amount, speed or *weight* of something

**melt** (v.)
to become *liquid*. If ice *melts*, it becomes water.

**microbe** (n.)
*Microbes* are very small living things. You cannot see them.

**mineral** (n.)
a natural thing that comes out of the ground, for example salt or gold

**molecule** (n.)
A *molecule* is made when two or more *atoms* of *chemical elements* come together.

**orbit** (v. and n.)
to move in a circle in *space*. *Orbit* is the noun of the verb *orbit*.

**particle** (n.)
a very small piece of *matter* or a very small part of an *atom*

**planet** (n.)
a large, round thing in space. Earth is a *planet*.

**plastic** (n.)
*Plastic* is strong and light. It is made in factories and used to make a lot of things that we use every day, for example bags and cups.

**powerful** (adj.)
strong and able to do things

**pressure** (n.)
the *force* that a *liquid* or gas makes when it presses against something

**probe** (n.)
a small *spaceship* with no one inside it. *Probes* send information to Earth.

**process** (n.)
a group of things that happen one after the other and *cause* a change or result

**protein** (n.)
*Proteins* are in meat, fish, cheese and eggs. Our bodies need *proteins* to make them grow and be strong.

**release** (v.)
to let *energy*, gas or another thing go into the area around it

**satellite** (n.)
We send *satellites* into *space*. They *orbit planets* and send pictures and information to Earth.

**shine** (v.)
1. If the Sun, Moon, *stars* or other *planets shine*, they give light.
2. to point the light from something towards a place

**smooth** (adj.)
A *smooth surface* is flat and doesn't have holes or high pieces in it.

**Solar System** (n.)
a part of *space* with the Sun and eight *planets*. These *planets orbit* the Sun. Earth is in the *Solar System*.

**solid** (adj.)
hard like rock, and not *liquid* or gas

**space** (n.)
the place outside Earth. The Sun and other *planets* are there.

**spaceship** (n.)
a plane or ship for *space*. A *spaceship* travels into *space*.

**star** (n.)
a very bright ball of gas. You see *stars* in the sky at night.

**surface** (n.)
the top or outside part of something

**telescope** (n.)
A *telescope* makes things that are a very long way from you look bigger or nearer so that you can see them.

**temperature** (n.)
how hot or cold something or someone is

**theory** (n.)
an idea that tries to explain why something happens

**tide** (n.)
when the sea moves towards land and away from it every day

**universe** (n.)
the world and everything outside it, like the Sun, Moon, *planets* and *stars*

**volcano** (n.)
a mountain with a big hole at the top. Fire, gas and hot rock sometimes come out of it.

**wave** (n.)
a piece of sound, light, heat or other *energy* that travels in a special way

**weight** (n.)
how heavy something or someone is

**worm** (n.); **wormhole** (n.)
A *worm* is a small animal with a long, thin, soft body and no legs which lives in earth. A *wormhole* is a hole made by a *worm*. Scientists use *wormhole* to describe a special way of going from one place in the *universe* to another place.

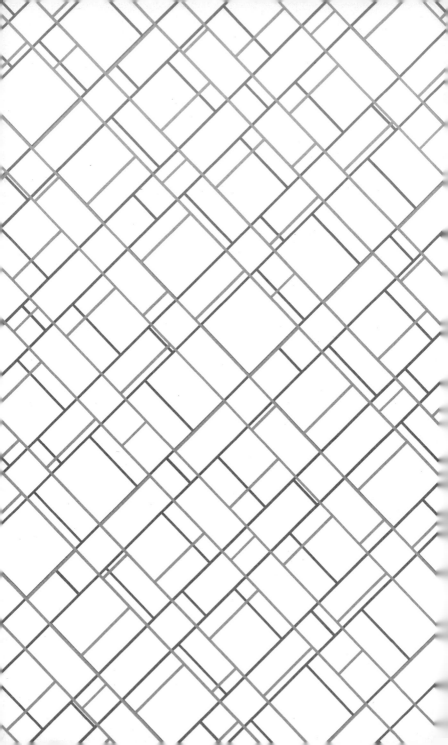

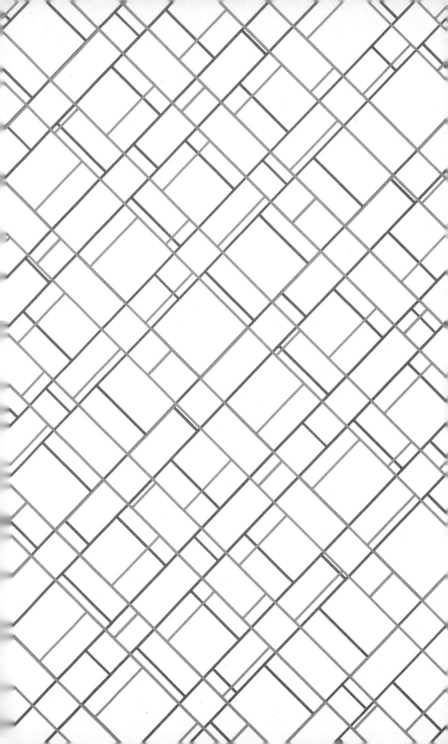

# Penguin 🐧 Readers

Visit **www.penguinreaders.co.uk**
for FREE Penguin Readers resources
and digital and audio versions of this book.